Book 1

Listening activities for the classroom

QUESTIONS
PUBLISHING

The Questions Publishing Company Ltd, 27 Frederick Street, Birmingham B1 3HH

The Questions Publishing Company Ltd
27 Frederick Street, Birmingham B1 3HH

First published in 2001

ISBN: 1-84190-076-1

Writing and editorial team: Linda Evans
                                     Katherine Pate
                                     Amanda Greenley

Sequences 1–5 scripted and recorded by: Phil Viner
                                          Jools Viner
                                          SmartPass

Design and illustration: Ivan Morison

Printed in the UK

Contents page

LISTEN UP!

Introduction

Listening is an important skill for everyone, particularly so in the school situation where so much information is given verbally. Yet many youngsters seem to have under-developed listening skills and teachers sometimes despair of having to repeat instructions, or give an explanation, three or four times.

Can listening skills be developed?

Well yes, but with some children these skills have to be taught and practised explicitly, rather than competency being taken for granted. It will be useful to demonstrate to youngsters how we often hear something extra when we listen a second or third time, how we can listen selectively and how visualising what we hear can help us to remember information.

These activities are designed for use with individuals, small groups or classes of pupils in KS 3 or at the top end of KS 2. They are fun to do and take up only a small amount of time (as with most things, 'little and often' is probably better than infrequent, lengthy sessions). Teachers may consider designating a regular 'listening time' slotted into a registration period or PSHE lesson; the activities are also particularly relevant to the English curriculum.

Listen Up! aims to:

*   improve pupils' listening skills,

*   develop their concentration span,

*   provide practice in visualisation skills,

*   improve memory skills, and

*   develop thinking skills.

There are twenty listening activities divided into two sections:

*   The first five sequences have been recorded onto CD by professional actors. These provide a rich listening experience, enhanced with sound effects and can also be used as a stimulus for creative writing activities. Each has a set of photocopiable activity sheets and there are extension suggestions on pages 2 and 3.

*   Activities 6–20 present shorter, less complex tasks, each with a photocopiable sheet for pupil use and a script for the teacher/support assistant to read.

Teacher's notes: Activities 1–5

The activities are not in any particular order of difficulty or length, but present a variety of listening experiences and accompanying tasks.

It may be useful for teachers to copy the recorded sequences from CD to tape for ease of 'pausing' and re-starting. Copyright law allows for one copy to be made per Listen Up! pack purchased.

It will be valuable for the teacher to listen to the recording before using it with a group of pupils, to ascertain its suitability and the most effective way of using it.

1. **The monarchs' room** (approx. 18 mins plus questions) Script pages 4–7, activities pages 8–11.

    A guide leads a group of youngsters around a stately home; in the monarchs' room, he shows them portraits of Edward I (5 mins), Henry VIII (6 mins), Elizabeth I (3 mins) and Queen Victoria (4 mins), and gives them some information about each one.

    This is the longest of the recorded passages and teachers may decide to play it through to the end, then replay one section at a time. Pupils can be asked to make notes of key facts as they listen, then answer the questions, or they can listen to the recording a second time and answer the questions as they go along.

    As an extension activity, particularly for the more able, pupils can be asked to script/record a similar commentary on other monarchs or famous historical figures – remembering to inject a little humour where appropriate and making it as interesting as possible.

2. **The funfair** (approx. 8 mins plus questions) Script pages 12 and 13, activities pages 14–17.

    Two youngsters visit the fair and have a go on the various stalls and attractions – particularly the Ghost Train. Listeners have to keep a running total of the money spent by the girl, Jenny, in order to answer the questions at the end.

    Activity 2b can lead into creative writing and 2d requires pupils to synthesise information they have heard, alongside their own experience of fairgrounds, to design posters advertising the fair.

    More able pupils may be able to compare this kind of travelling fair with its modern counterpart – theme parks.

3. **Suspects** (approx. 10 mins plus questions) Script pages 18 and 19, activities pages 20–23.

    The police are investigating a bank robbery and find that a blind witness can give them useful information. The 'identity parade' at the end is carried out by voice identification rather than visual recognition.

    Activity 3b requires listeners to trace the route taken by the witness on her way to the bank. Pupils can also be asked to work out a set of directions for the police to follow when they drive Mrs Webber home from the police station. Activity 3c probably needs to be done as pupils are listening to the recording; activity 3d can lead into a number of creative writing activities.

    An extension activity for more able pupils might be to ask them how, as town planners, they would consider the needs of blind and partially sighted people to make it easier for them to get around.

4. **The fall on Franwell Moor** (approx. 8 mins plus questions) Script pages 24 and 25, activities pages 26–29.

    Jackie's father falls while they are walking on the moors and she has to run for help.

Teacher's notes: Activities 1–5

The questions for this sequence are divided into sections, with 11–20 requiring pupils to infer and hypothesise from what they hear. They also need to empathise with the characters and use logical thinking.

The memory exercise, activity 4d, indicates some of the strategies for improving short-term memory (see also the use of mnemonics in sequence 1) and can be used in many other situations where pupils need to remember facts.

5. **Shopping** (approx. 7 mins plus questions) Script pages 30 and 31, activities pages 32–37

    Mother and son are shopping for various items and listeners are asked to keep a count of the money being spent. The working-out is structured for pupils who need some support and the questions have multiple-choice answers, which may be easier for some pupils than having to write their own responses.

    The last activity, which requires pupils to plan a new High Street, is suitable for even the most able pupils and presents opportunities for logical thinking and hypothesising. Pupils may be asked to justify their ideas for the benefit of the 'planning committee', and/or compare their different plans and argue their point of view. A further extension could involve them in debate: 'This house proposes that out-of-town retail parks mean commercial ruin for small retailers'.

The teacher's knowledge of the group or class will dictate the best way of using the recorded sequences.

It may be appropriate to play the entire sequence through once, then replay (perhaps a little at a time, or a section at a time in the case of 'The monarchs' room') to allow pupils to answer questions on the activity sheet. A third playing will allow pupils to check their answers. More able pupils may need to listen only once.

*   Pupils can be encouraged to make notes as they listen, or jot down key words (the teacher will need to decide whether to focus purely on listening skills or whether to introduce short-term memory practice as well).

*   The tasks have been designed to minimise the amount of writing required – and in some cases oral answers may be more suitable.

*   There is scope within each recording for role play, with pupils working in pairs or the teacher taking on the 'mantle of the expert' and answering questions 'in character'.

*   There are opportunities in each activity for developing both creative and critical thinking skills to varying extents: sorting, categorising and synthesising information; developing empathy; using inference; analysis; visualisation and problem solving.

Extension activities

Ask pupils to:

*   listen for all of the non-verbal sounds in a sequence and list them;

*   make up a set of questions for another group;

*   write and record their own script for a listening activity, with sound effects;

*   listen for particular words and their explanations, or find out their meanings for a follow-up activity (perhaps homework);

*   list the different characters heard in the sequence – supply names if they are not given;

*   write a sequel, continuing the style and theme.

The monarchs' room

Listen Up! guide: SShhhh! We're in a stately home. That's a fine old house owned by a grand family and they keep it a little bit like a museum, so the public can come and nose about and learn about the history of the family and the area.

This stately home has a very important room, the monarchs' room, full of portraits of the kings and queens of Britain. Look there, that man's a guide and he's about to take a school group in – let's follow a student inside and listen with them. And remember – listen up to what the guide says because I'll be asking you questions at the end – so, open your ears!

Gallery guide: Come along, come along, are we all in? Good, now this is the room where we have portraits of the kings and queens of British history – the monarchs' room – oh that comes from the Greek 'monarch', it means one chief.

This magnificent portrait here is of Edward I, who ruled England from 1272 to 1307.

John: Seven hundred years ago.

Gallery guide: He was a wonderful king – they called him Longshanks because he was so tall. At the age of 15 he was married to Eleanor, the Infanta of Castile.

John: Infa-what?

Gallery guide: Infanta. A young princess in Spain was called the Infanta. She was only 13 years old when she married Edward. And it's funny you should say 'infa-what' because at the time, the English heard 'Infanta of Castile' and thought it sounded like Elephant and Castle, and that got repeated and repeated and stuck – today there are many pubs all over the country called the Elephant and Castle as well as an area in London – and that's where they get their name from. Funny eh! Another very interesting story about Edward I is that he led a crusade to the Holy Land…

…and during this he was wounded by a dagger tipped with poison.
He was saved by Eleanor who, so the story goes, sucked the poison from the wound and spat it away.

John: Yuk!

Gallery guide: But it wasn't just for adventures abroad that he was famous – he was an important king at home too. In 1295 he established the first model parliament, which is the ancestor of today's democratic parliament.
It's also important to know that, at this time, all the countries we now know as Britain were separate: Wales, England, Scotland and Ireland.
Edward conquered Wales in 1284. Then in 1296 his forces marched into Scotland and seized the Stone of Scone, which was an important symbol of Scottish kingship. For hundreds of years all Scottish kings had been invested, that means to be made king, within sight of the Scone Stone – so you can see how angry the Scots would have been.

John: It's a bit like them coming and stealing the crown jewels, isn't it?

Gallery guide: Exactly, and Edward's men carried the stone back to England, to Westminster Abbey, where it stayed for 700 years before it was returned to Scotland.
Now, those of you who have seen the film 'Braveheart' will know about this time because after the Stone of Scone was taken, a Scottish rebellion was led by William Wallace, who was played by Mel Gibson in the movie. He was a thorn in Edward's side until his capture and execution in 1305.
Despite his success as monarch there was personal sadness for the king as his much loved wife Eleanor died in 1290. She passed away near Grantham and her body was carried back to London. Of course, this is long before trains and cars and it took twelve days and nights to reach the capital.
At each place they stopped for the night, Edward had a large cross built as a memorial for his queen. The most famous are Waltham Cross and Charing Cross.
Edward and Eleanor had sixteen children, yet when Edward died of dysentery in 1307 only four were alive – three daughters and one son, who would become Edward II.
Right, let's move on to another portrait and this time…

LISTEN UP!

The monarchs' room Teacher's script

John: It's Henry the Eighth. I recognise him. The big belly and beard, and the colourful outfit.

Gallery guide: So we pass from the greatest of the Plantagenet kings to the greatest of the Tudor kings: Henry VIII, who ruled from April 22nd 1509 to January 28th 1547. As a child he was not heir to the throne because he had an older brother, Arthur, who should have been king when their father died. Henry, as a boy, was intended to join the church and so received a classical education; he spoke both French and German. He was also a musician and it is believed that he wrote the music of 'Greensleeves' – you know (hums a bit). Yet he never became a priest, as tragedy struck the royal family when his brother Arthur died. This meant Henry was heir to the throne and at the age of seventeen he became king, crowned Henry VIII. It was one of his father's last wishes that Henry marry his brother Arthur's widow, Katherine of Aragon, and this he did. Now, does anybody know anything about Henry VIII?

John: He had six wives.

Gallery guide: Very good – yes, he had six wives. But what most people don't realise is that he was married to his first wife Katherine for 24 years. They had six children yet only one, a daughter, Mary, survived infancy. The others all died while still babies. Henry wanted a male heir. He felt that a queen running the country would undo the great work he had done to stabilise England, to make it strong. But England was a Catholic country and Henry was a loyal Catholic and by Catholic law he could not divorce his wife. But he desperately needed a son, so he broke with his faith, and with tradition, and established a new church – the Church of England. With these new powers he annulled his marriage to Katherine and married Anne Boleyn. She became pregnant very quickly but had a daughter, Elizabeth, who was later to become Elizabeth I. Two more children were born to Anne yet they both died quickly. After three years of marriage to Anne, Henry was even more desperate for a son and he had his second marriage declared invalid. Anne Boleyn was charged with treason and executed – beheaded in the Tower of London. Just eleven days later he married wife number three – Jane Seymour. She fell pregnant so quickly there wasn't even time to arrange her coronation – a ceremony to crown her queen. Finally Jane Seymour gave Henry what he longed for – a son, Edward, who later would become Edward VI. The birth, however, had complications and Jane died soon after.

Many years later, when Henry died, he was laid beside Jane in St George's Chapel, Westminster. She was his favourite, probably because she had given him the son he yearned for.

Now that Henry had his son at last, he turned his attention back to Europe where many countries threatened England. They were angered at Henry's decision to get rid of the Roman Catholic Church and put his own version of it in its place.

So, in January 1540 Henry, to make friends with Europe, married Anne of Cleeves, a German noblewoman. The marriage was not happy however, it was purely political.

John: That means Henry didn't fancy her.

Gallery guide: After seven months of their sham marriage, they were divorced.

Henry didn't waste any time in finding wife number five and only three weeks after his divorce from Anne of Cleeves he married Katherine Howard, a teenage cousin of Anne Boleyn.

John: Anne Boleyn was his second wife, the one who was beheaded in the Tower of London.

Gallery guide: That's right. Well, her cousin Katherine ended her days the same way. She was tried for treason in February 1542 and executed. Henry was then 51 years old and marriage to a teenager hadn't worked, so he married an older woman, another Katherine. Katherine Parr outlived her husband.

Henry died at the age of 55, on the 28th of January 1547. He was the first king to be called 'his majesty' and left behind a more modern and stronger country.

Now, when I was at school we remembered the wives by using a little saying:

'Anulled, beheaded, died, divorced, beheaded, survived'. And there were three Katherines, two Annes and one Jane.

Let's move on to the next portrait shall we? It's someone I've already mentioned. That's her picture, with the flaming red hair – Elizabeth I – daughter of Henry VIII and his second wife, Anne Boleyn.

But Elizabeth didn't become queen directly after her father's death – oh no, there were three monarchs between Henry and Elizabeth. First, the son Henry had longed for, Edward VI, who was on the throne for six years, from 1547 to 1553.
Then there was Lady Jane Grey who was on the throne for only nine days. Then Mary, the daughter of Henry and Katherine of Aragon, ruled for five years until November 1558 when she died, leaving her half-sister Elizabeth to rule for the next 45 years.

John: That was a long time to rule back then.

Gallery guide: That's certainly true, because people didn't live as long as we do today. But let me get back to Queen Elizabeth's reign. She was known as 'good Queen Bess, the virgin queen' because she never married or had children. Under her rule it was a golden age, with much exploration and discovery of the Earth. Sir Walter Raleigh explored the New World of America and brought back the potato and tobacco. Sir Francis Drake sailed round South America and the East Indies and brought back jewels and gold. He also defeated the Spanish Armada in 1588 and made England the 'ruler of the seas'.
It was also during Elizabeth's reign that William Shakespeare wrote his plays and poems and the Globe Theatre was built in London.
Though Elizabeth was very popular with her people, there were several assassination attempts on her life, and in 1570 the Pope excommunicated her and said that anyone who managed to kill her would go to heaven! Imagine!
Now, as we said earlier, she ruled to a grand old age, but towards the end of her life Elizabeth was afraid of growing old and wore a wig even redder than her own hair had once been. She used white powder on her skin to cover her smallpox scars, though nothing could be done to disguise her teeth, which had rotted away due to her love of sweet things.

John: Gross.

Gallery guide: Elizabeth I died in 1603 and as she had no direct heir to the throne – remember she had not married and had no children – it passed to James VI of Scotland, who then became James I of England
Let's move on to the next portrait shall we? Now this is a very different portrait. Why is it so different?

John: Well, instead of being dressed in beautiful colours and with gold and jewels she's dressed in black. She looks old and so sad.

Gallery guide: That's right. This is Queen Victoria who is famous for saying:

Victoria: We are not amused.

Gallery guide: It's probably just a myth though and she never actually said it.
Now, we thought Elizabeth I was queen for a long time.

John: 45 years.

Gallery guide: Well remembered. Yes, Victoria beats that, in fact she is the longest ruling of all monarchs (remember, that means king or queen). She was queen for 63 years, from 1837 to 1901. This portrait was painted towards the end of her reign and she was in mourning for her husband, Albert, who had died and left her sad and quite lonely. In fact her husband died in 1861, a full 40 years before she herself died, and she wore black mourning clothes for the rest of her life, never forgetting him.

John: No wonder she looks so miserable. Is Albert the same Albert of the Albert Hall, where the Proms come from?

Gallery guide: Oh yes. When he died Victoria wanted to commemorate his life, so she had the Albert Hall and the Albert Memorial built. But probably the greatest memorial is the Victoria and Albert Museum, which was his idea. You see, Albert was a great forward thinker and a highly moral man. When he and Victoria married in 1840 they set about influencing the government to reform Britain – to make it better. The rule of Victoria was a time of greatness for Britain in many ways, but most especially in health, education and technology. And Albert was an important figure in the move for British technology. It was his idea for the Great Exhibition in 1851, the first World's Fair, which was both a display of Britain's greatness but also a talking-shop where inventors and industrialists could plan and talk together. It was not only a success in what it encouraged but an immense public event; everybody wanted to go to the Great Exhibition. So, it made a great deal of money, which Albert used to finance the Victoria and Albert Museum in London.

The monarchs' room   Teacher's script

John: I've been there, it was pretty good but afterwards we went to the Natural History Museum and saw the dinosaurs.

Gallery guide: The Victorian age was the time of Britain's greatest influence in the world. Victoria's people loved her – in contrast to the monarchs directly before her. In fact when Victoria came to the throne there were three assassination attempts upon her life in the first four years. But once Albert was by her side and the government moved towards popular reform, she just grew and grew in popularity.

The Crimean War of 1854 to 1856 was a great sadness of her reign, yet she herself gained much public admiration with her instigation of the Victoria Cross – a medal given for bravery. Each of these crosses was made from the cast iron of guns captured from the enemy.

Victoria was also something of a writer and produced two books about her beloved Balmoral, the Scottish home for her and Albert. She died in 1901, having seen in the new century as Queen of the British Empire, Empress of India and possibly the most significant monarch Britain has ever had. Right, that's it for this room. Shall we move on to another? Every single room has something fascinating that brings history to life.

Listen Up! guide: Let's tiptoe away now and leave them to the rest of the tour. Well that was great, so much information – I hope you listened hard to him as he told us about the four important monarchs from history. And you remember what monarch means don't you?… That's right 'one chief'. And it comes from which ancient language?… Yes from ancient Greek.

Now, let's see how well you listened. I am going to ask you some questions, 20 in all – that's five about each monarch. You can read them on activity sheet 1a.

I'll read them through with you, then you might want to hear the recording again and write your answers as you go along.

1. When did Edward I rule – between which years? And which century was that? Remember, if he was born in the twelve hundreds, that means he was born in the thirteenth century. He died in the thirteen hundreds so he died in the fourteenth century. OK.

2. Now he had a nickname – and he got it because he was tall. What was it?

3. Do you remember the name of his wife? Write down her first name and the title she had in Spain before she married.

4. She saved her husband's life at one point too, didn't she? What happened to him?

5. Edward's army marched into Scotland and they took a famous relic. What was it?

Great, now let's move on to the next monarch we saw, that was Henry VIII.

6. When did Henry VIII rule, which years and which century was that in?

7. How long was he married to his first wife, Katherine of Aragon?

8. When he decided to divorce his wife, Henry turned his back on the Catholic faith and started his own religion. What was that religion called?

9. Now we know Henry had many wives, don't we? How many were there – can you remember that little rhyme the art gallery guide gave us? Well let's see if you can list each wife in order, in the table we've drawn out for you.

10. Henry wrote a famous piece of music. What was it called?

Excellent, so now let's consider Henry's daughter, Elizabeth I.

11. What was her nickname?

12. How long did she reign?

13. What did Sir Walter Raleigh bring back from the New World while Elizabeth was queen?

14. Which famous writer wrote in Elizabethan times and is best known for working at the Globe Theatre in London?

15. Who defeated the Spanish Armada in 1588?

That's great. Let's move on to our final portrait shall we? Queen Victoria. Now she holds a record as British monarch doesn't she? She is the longest reigning monarch.

16. How many years was she on the throne?

17. She is famous for a saying that she probably never said. What was it?

18. She was a sad woman after the death of her husband. How did she show that sadness to the public?

19. What was her husband's name?

20. He organised a popular event. What was it called?

Well, that's that – all 20 questions. I hope you did really well. It's time to leave the stately home now, but keep listening. You'll be hearing from me.

The monarchs' room Activity sheet 1a

Name:_____ Date:_____

Edward I

1. When did Edward I rule – between which years? And which century was that?

   _____

2. Now he had a nickname – and he got it because he was tall. What was it? _____

3. Do you remember the name of his wife? Write down her first name and the title she had in Spain before she married.

   _____

4. She saved her husband's life at one point too, didn't she? What happened to him? _____

5. Edward's army marched into Scotland and they took a famous relic. What was it? _____

Henry VIII

6. When did Henry VIII rule, which years and which century was that in? _____

7. How long was he married to his first wife, Katherine of Aragon?

   _____

8. When he decided to divorce his wife, Henry turned his back on the Catholic faith and started his own religion. What was that religion called? _____

9. Now we know Henry had many wives, don't we? How many were there – can you remember that little rhyme the art gallery guide gave us? Well let's see if you can list each wife in order, in the table we've drawn out for you.

annulled	beheaded	died	divorced	beheaded	survived

10. Henry wrote a famous piece of music. What was it called?

   _____

The monarchs' room Activity sheet 1a

Name:_____ Date:_____

Elizabeth I

11. What was her nickname?

_____

12. How long did she reign?

_____

13. What did Sir Walter Raleigh bring back from the New World
while Elizabeth was queen?

_____

14. Which famous writer wrote in Elizabethan times and is best
known for working at the Globe Theatre in London?

_____

15. Who defeated the Spanish Armada in 1588?

_____

Queen Victoria

16. How many years was she on the throne? _____

17. She is famous for a saying that she probably never said. What
was it? _____

18. She was a sad woman after the death of her husband.
How did she show that sadness to the public?

_____

19. What was her husband's name? _____

20. He organised a popular event. What was it called?

_____

The monarchs' room Activity sheet 1b

Name:_____   Date:_____

Can you fill in this table?

Name	Born	Died	Married to..	Children	Enemies	Remembered for..
Edward I						
Henry VIII						
Elizabeth I						
Victoria						

LISTEN UP!

The monarchs' room   Activity sheet 1c

Name:_____   Date:_____

An illustrator is going to draw the four monarchs and asks you for some information about their appearances. What can you tell him?

	size	hair	complexion	clothes
Edward I				
Henry VIII				
Elizabeth I				
Victoria				

Discussion and role play

- If you could travel in a time machine to meet one of these monarchs, which one would you choose and why?

- Imagine that you have to interview the monarch and write it up as an article for the school magazine. What questions would you ask?

- Role play: in pairs, decide who will be the interviewer and who will be the monarch and role play the interview. The 'monarch' should try to be as accurate as possible with his or her answers – based on what you have learned from the recording and any extra information you have gathered.

LISTEN UP!

The funfair

Listen Up! guide: Wow, look at that sunset! The whole sky is pink with little red shafts in it. It's dusk – you know, that time just before it's dark when the sun has gone down but there are just those last few rays in the sky. Soon it will be dark, which is just perfect as the lights on the funfair go on across the field – look there's the Wurlitzer, all lit up, and the helter skelter. And now I can just hear the music from the carousel – can you? Listen hard for it. And listen hard for the whole scene. We are joining Jenny and her mum as they walk across the field from their house towards the fair. Jenny is itching to get there, she loves the fair and is meeting her friend Paul there. Let's follow Jenny, and listen to what she does and who she meets, because I will be asking you question afterwards. OK, let's go to the fair…

Jenny: Come on, come on I want to get to the fair quickly.

Mum: Jenny it's not going anywhere is it? It's there all weekend.
So what do you want to see especially?

Jenny: You know what my favourite is.

Mum: Oh yes, you like to be scared.

Jenny: I love to be scared. I hope they've got a Ghost Train or a Haunted House – or both.
I've saved up my pocket money and have £8 to spend. Mum can't you walk faster – or jog a bit? Paul will be waiting for me.

Mum: Jenny! Well go on, run off if you have to. I'll get a cup of tea and then come and find you.

Jenny: Thanks mum.

Listen Up! guide: The fair is enormous, full of rides and stalls. As Jenny makes her way towards the rides you might want to make notes about who she meets and what they say. Don't write sentences, key words will do – they are a great way to help you remember and answer questions later.

Jenny: Hi Paul, have you been waiting long? I couldn't get my mum to go any faster.

Paul: No, only about five minutes – I've been watching them on the skittle alley.

Skittle man: Three balls for a pound, come on now, try your arm at skittles – win a lovely cuddly toy. Now then, you two look like good bowlers – are you having a go sir? Win something for the pretty young lady.

Paul: Not for her but my little sister would love one. Go on then, I'll have a go. Here's a pound.

Jenny: And I'll have the same. I bet I do better than you.

Paul: Oh no – so near and yet so far, only one skittle left standing.

Jenny: Yessss! I am the champion, girls are the greatest. I'll have a giant teddy please.

Skittle man: Well done. I said you looked like a good'un.

Jenny: Here you are Paul, give this to your sister – I've already got too many fluffy toys in my bedroom. Mum says I've got to clear some of them out. I just wanted to beat you.

Paul: Well I think it should be best out of three.

Jenny: No, you should just take your defeat like a man, and the bear for Saskia.

Paul: OK then, thanks – she'll love it.

Sweet seller: Candyfloss, toffee apples, fudge.

Mirror man: Hall of mirrors, hall of weird and wonderful looking glasses that bend and bobble, distort and delight. See yourself as a giant or a gnome. See yourself upside down and back to front.

Jenny: Shall we go in?

Paul: No, let's go on to the shooting gallery instead, I want to get even.

Shooting gallery man: Rootin', tootin' shootin' gallery – come on now, just like the wild, wild west. Roll up, roll up. One pound buys you three shots – burst two balloons and you're a winner.

Paul: I'll take three shots please.

Shooting gallery man: Three shots it is, there…

Paul: Whoops!

Shooting gallery man: Careful now, don't want you killing your friend.

Paul: Oh, hopeless – I'm no better at shooting than knocking down skittles.

Coconut shy stall holder: Knock down a coconut and win a great prize – three balls for a pound – come on, come on. Hey there, young lady, want a go?

Jenny: They're stuck on with glue – I'm not that stupid!

Paul: Let's go and get some chips. Over there look see, next door to the…

Jenny: …Ghost Train. Come on Paul.

Ghost train attendant: Be chilled, be thrilled, and pray you aren't killed in the Ghost Train.

LISTEN UP!

Jenny: Two please. This is my treat.

Ghost train attendant: That's £3 to you madam. Sure you two will be all right in there?

Jenny: Of course we will. We're not babies, you know.

Ghost train attendant: As I live and breathe – I only just got out alive the first time I rode it.

Jenny: What happened?

Ghost train attendant: Now that would be telling – you'll just have to find out for yourselves. Hold on tight.

Listen Up! guide: And Jenny and Paul sit in their carriage shaped like a human skull as the doors slowly open and the train slides into the blackness.

Dracula: My name is Dracula and I vant to suck your blood.

Jenny: No way bloodsucking fiend – if I make a cross like this.

Frankenstein: I am Frankenstein. They created me from dead bodies and breathed life into me.

Paul: Get back monster.

Zombie: Errrrrrgh.

Jenny: Undead Zombie freak – keep away.

Witch: I will have your tongue for my cauldron.

Paul: No way witch.

Robespierre: They cut off my head.

Jenny: The guillotine! Oh no, all that blood.

Jenny: Werewolves! A silver bullet will see you off – so be careful.

Listen Up! guide: At last the train clangs through the doors and out into the open air. Jenny and Paul look terrified, their faces chalky white, and they're both trembling.

Ghost train attendant: Still alive then?

Jenny: No sweat – it was really tame.

Paul: Yeah. Tame… I thought that zombie looked – well, real.

Jenny: And that guillotine cutting the head off – was that a real head?

Ghost train attendant: If you would like to go in a second time it's on the house.

Jenny: It's free?

Ghost train attendant: Free? Well, no money will change hands – though there is a price to pay.

Jenny: No… no thank you, it's a very nice offer but…

Paul: Yes, yes we should get off – we have homework to do and…

Jenny: Oh look, there's mum must run. Come on. Let's see if she'll buy us an ice cream before we go on the dodgems.

Listen Up! guide: Well, I for one will not be going on any more Ghost Trains. That one sounded really spooky.

You might be braver though – are you? And did you listen hard? Well let's see what you remembered shall we. I am going to ask you some more questions. You can read along with me on activity sheet 2a if you like and use any notes you have made. So, let's start.

1. Jenny said she loved to be scared. What did she hope to see at the fair?

2. How much money has Jenny got to spend at the fair?

3. Jenny's mum let Jenny run on to the fair. What was mum going to do?

4. How long had Paul been waiting?

5. How much did it cost for three balls on the skittle alley?

6. Who won the giant teddy?

7. Who was the giant teddy a present for?

8. A sweet seller was shouting out what he had on his stall. What did he have?

9. How could people see themselves in the hall of mirrors?

10. How many balloons had to be burst to win a prize on the shooting gallery?

11. Why did Jenny choose not to have a go on the coconut shy?

12. What did the man who ran the Ghost Train say about it as Jenny approached?

13. Jenny and Paul are heading for the dodgems when they see her mum. What does Jenny want her mum to buy for them?

14. Is this a good idea do you think? What might be the consequences?

15. How much did Jenny spend altogether?

16. How much money did Jenny have left to pay for the dodgems and any other rides?

Listen Up! guide: Well, that is it for the funfair then. The next time a fair comes to your area go there and make a point of stopping in the middle. Close your eyes and listen, try and hear all the separate sounds that make up the mix. OK, I hope you did well and listened hard. You'll be hearing from me.

13

The funfair

Name:_____   Date:_____

1. Jenny said she loved to be scared. What did she hope to see at the fair? _____

2. How much money has Jenny got to spend at the fair? _____

3. Jenny's mum let Jenny run on to the fair. What was mum going to do? _____

4. How long had Paul been waiting? _____

5. How much did it cost for three balls on the skittle alley? _____

6. Who won the giant teddy? _____

7. Who was the giant teddy a present for? _____

8. A sweet seller was shouting out what he had on his stall. What did he have? _____

9. How could people see themselves in the hall of mirrors?

   _____

10. How many balloons had to be burst to win a prize on the shooting gallery? _____

11. Why did Jenny choose not to have a go on the coconut shy?

   _____

12. What did the man who ran the Ghost Train say about it as Jenny approached? _____

13. Jenny and Paul are heading for the dodgems when they see her mum. What does Jenny want her mum to buy for them?

   _____

14. Is this a good idea do you think? What might be the consequences?

   _____

15. How much did Jenny spend altogether? _____

16. How much money did Jenny have left to pay for the dodgems and any other rides? _____

LISTEN UP!

The funfair

Name:_____   Date:_____

How are these people feeling?
Write in the thought bubbles what
they might be thinking.

amused

sad

bored

scared

puzzled

uninterested

The funfair

Name:_____   Date:_____

'Ghouls Gallery'

Match the picture to the name and circle the ones
that Paul and Jenny saw in the Ghost Train.

zombie

witch

corpse

devil

severed hand

alien

giant spider

headless man

Dracula

werewolf

Frankenstein

ghost

goblin

LISTEN UP!

The funfair

Name:_____   Date:_____

Posters for the fair

Use this planning sheet to help you remember
all the things to mention:

Rides	Other attractions	To eat and drink
_____	_____	_____
_____	_____	_____
_____	_____	_____
_____	_____	_____
_____	_____	_____
_____	_____	_____
_____	_____	_____
_____	_____	_____
_____	_____	_____
_____	_____	_____
_____	_____	_____

Extension activity

Draw a monster or an alien with clearly defined features and
colours, (e.g. a large, round head with bulging red eyes and a
conical nose... a huge mouth with no lips and green fangs...).
Now, sit back-to-back with a partner and describe your monster
or alien so that your partner can draw it – see how well you can
describe it, and how well your partner can listen. Swap over and
see who produces the best/most accurate drawing.

Suspects

Listen Up! guide: Oooh it's a terrible night tonight, not a night to be out unless you have to. And tonight Detective Inspector Spring needs to be out and about as he's investigating a bank robbery. You know I think we should go and hear how he's getting on – and you will be able to help him find the robbers if you listen hard for the sound clues. OK, let's go...

Reporter: DI Spring, DI Spring... Detective Inspector Spring, do you have any leads to follow?

DI Spring: At this time we are interviewing each witness and following up on reports of the getaway car.

Reporter: Do you have any suspects?

DI Spring: At this time I cannot give out that kind of information.

Reporter: Well, do you expect to make arrests soon?

DI Spring: We are confident that our witnesses will give us the information we need to track down these criminals.

Reporter: But what kind of evidence do you have? I understand the robbers all wore masks.

DI Spring: That is correct, rubber masks.

Reporter: Rubber masks of the seven dwarves to be exact.

DI Spring: The seven dwarves, that is right.

Reporter: So you have no eye witness to identify the robbers.

DI Spring: Eye witness. No you are right there. We have no eye witness who saw the faces of these men.

Reporter: So what do you have DI Spring?

DI Spring: Ah, you will have to wait and see.

Policewoman sergeant: So what 'ave we got guv?

DI Spring: Well, we've looked at the CCTV camera footage but no luck. All the men were wearing rubber dwarf masks, all seven of them. The masks and the clothing were found in a dustbin outside the Pizza Palace in the high street. No witnesses and no fingerprints.

Policewoman sergeant: And in the bank all the witnesses were forced to lie face down on the floor.

DI Spring: That's right, none of them saw a thing.

Policewoman sergeant: Then why have you called for an identity parade for tonight at nine o'clock? You know something, don't you guv?

DI Spring: Well Sergeant, what I know is that one of the witnesses, Mrs Webber, is blind.

Policewoman sergeant: Blind. Blind... Oh, you mean that because she is blind her other senses are stronger. Taste and touch and sense of smell...

DI Spring: And most importantly – her sense of hearing. Come into my office, Sergeant. This is Mrs Webber, the witness I was telling you about. Mrs Webber could you repeat what you told me earlier?

Mrs Webber: Certainly. Well, I left my house at 12 o'clock and turned left down Weston Hill, then right into Sandwell Street.

DI Spring: Excuse me Mrs Webber, how do you know what the exact time was.

Mrs Webber: Because of the church clock – it was chiming you see, just as I left my doorstep.

DI Spring: Please continue.

Mrs Webber: At the traffic lights, I made my way straight across on the pelican crossing then, at the island, I took the third road on the left – Castle Road. I have to be careful there.

DI Spring: You're sure it was Castle Road?

Mrs Webber: Of course, I went that way to go into the pet shop for some bird seed. They've got a cockatoo in the window that says the funniest things.

Cockatoo: Who's a pretty boy then?

Mrs Webber: At the next roundabout, I went right, which brings me alongside the cemetery, then crossed the main road into the park. I found a bench and sat down just on 1.40pm.

DI Spring: Now how did you know it was 1.40?

Mrs Webber: Somebody in the park was listening to a radio and a cricket match was on. The players were just about to start the afternoon session – so it was 1.40. After a while, it got a bit chilly and I walked down Strathdene Road to buy a newspaper at the newsagents in Weston Avenue. I like the Herald. My next-door neighbour usually pops in at teatime and reads bits of it to me. I called into Jan's Café on the Ash Road for a cup of tea, then I went to the National Bank on Kemberton Road. I was in the queue at 2pm.

DI Spring: And the evidence to prove it was 2pm?

Mrs Webber: Well, the bank manager, an old friend of mine, is a stickler for punctuality and I heard him walking out of his office.

Bank manager: Lunchtime Edna, back in an hour at 3.

Mrs Webber: And it was seconds later that all hell broke loose.

Sleepy: This is a robbery, everybody face down on the floor – no heroics, don't be stupid and everybody will have stories to tell their grandchildren.

Dopey: You, behind the counter. No alarms, no booby traps, just put the money into these bags and you'll be OK. Just notes, all you've got beside you – each window – now move it.

Dopey: Everybody, and I mean everybody, on the floor and count slowly to ten thousand before you get up.

Listen Up! guide: What an incredible noise there is as the bank robbers force the cashiers to fill bags with money and the customers to lie face down on the floor. Of course the customers are all too frightened to listen to

two of the robbers as they begin to chat to each other. In this din nobody could hear a conversation could they? Except Mrs Webber of course. She is calm and has concentrated hearing and listens to the two robbers as they talk.

Bashful: I hope this all goes smoothly, it's our anniversary tonight.

Happy: You and Linda – how long is it?

Bashful: Ten years. But six of 'em was in the nick, so I owe 'er a good night. I've bought 'er a fur coat – mink – you know, dead expensive.

Happy: And you're going out for dinner?

Bashful: Yeah, reservations at Albertinis at 8 with cold champagne at the table and a violinist booked just for us. Choice.

Sleepy: OK time's up, let's get out of here.

Dopey: Right, let's go.

DI Spring: Now, Mrs Webber I've looked at the CCTV tapes of the robbery. There were seven robbers, each a different dwarf. Two of them, Doc and Sneezy were posted on the doors to look out for the police. Another two dwarves, Dopey and Grumpy, dealt with the cashiers and grabbed the money. Now you and your fellow customers dropped to the floor where you were queuing and two dwarves, Bashful and Happy, covered you. Leaving the last dwarf, Sleepy, in the centre of the room. He seemed to be in charge. Now what did you hear that can be used to identify the robbers?

Mrs Webber: While I was laying there, the two robbers who were closest, Bashful and Happy, were talking.

Bashful: I hope this all goes smoothly, it's our anniversary tonight

Happy: You and Linda – how long is it?

Bashful: Ten years. But six of 'em was in the nick, so I owe 'er a good night. I've bought 'er a fur coat – mink – you know, dead expensive.

Happy: And you're going out for dinner?

Bashful: Yeah, reservations at Albertinis at 8 with cold champagne at the table and a violinist booked just for us. Choice.

DI Spring: Thank you Mrs Webber. And tonight at 8pm I can tell you that we arrested, in the establishment of Albertinis, one Andrew 'Chopper' Coles who was dining with his wife of ten years, Linda, and she was wearing a fur coat, though it was not mink but a cheap imitation bought at the market. Now Mrs Webber, I will ask you to come to an identification parade. You will hear six men and I will ask you to pick out the robber you heard.

Policewoman sergeant: Now you lot, from left to right, repeat the lines written on the card. Go.

Listen Up! guide: Now, I want all of you to listen very hard with Mrs Webber. Can you pick out the bank robber?

Policewoman sergeant: Now you number one.

One: I hope this all goes smoothly, it's our anniversary tonight.

Policewoman sergeant: Now number two.

Two: I hope this all goes smoothly, it's our anniversary tonight.

Policewoman sergeant: Now number three.

Three: I hope this all goes smoothly, it's our anniversary tonight.

Policewoman sergeant: Now number four.

Four: I hope this all goes smoothly, it's our anniversary tonight.

Policewoman sergeant: Now number five.

Five: I hope this all goes smoothly, it's our anniversary tonight.

Policewoman sergeant: Now number six.

Six: I hope this all goes smoothly, it's our anniversary tonight.

Listen Up! guide: So, there are the six voices to choose from. On activity sheet 3a there's a picture of the robber. Write in which number you think the bank robber was.

Did you pick out the right one? If you listened hard you should have – but let's just see how well you did listen as I have some more questions to ask you.

You can read along with them if you like on activity sheet 3a. Let's go.

1. How many robbers were there?
2. What sort of masks were they wearing?
3. Where were the masks found later?
4. All the bank customers were made to do something by the bank robbers. What was that?
5. What is the name of the Detective Inspector leading the investigation?
6. At what time did Mrs Webber set out from her house?
7. In the park, Mrs Webber listens to the radio. What is happening on it?
8. What does she buy from the newsagents?
9. Who does the bank manager call out to as he leaves his office? Is it a) Marge b) Edna c) Hilary.
10. Where was the robber arrested?
11. Who was he with?
12. How many men were in the identity parade?

Listen Up! guide: On activity sheet 3b, you will see a map of the area where the robbery took place. Listen to the recording again and trace in the route taken by Mrs Webber. Fill in the clock times as you hear them and draw in some of the features mentioned: the church, the pelican crossing, the pet shop, the newsagent's and the bank

Activity sheet 3c shows the CCTV image inside the bank. Write in the name of each dwarf and show where they all stood as the robbery took place.

There are some other activities for you to try on activity sheet 3d – enjoy!

Right, that's it from the police station. Detective Inspector Spring was very glad you could help. It's amazing how listening can help isn't it? I hope you did well with these questions and listened hard all the way through.

You'll be hearing from me!

Name:_____   Date:_____

Here's a picture of the robber.
Write on the card he's holding
his number from the identification
parade.

1. How many robbers were there?   _____

2. What sort of masks were they wearing?   _____

3. Where were the masks found later?   _____

4. All the bank customers were made to do something
    by the bank robbers. What was that?   _____

5. What is the name of the Detective Inspector
    leading the investigation?   _____

6. At what time did Mrs Webber set out from her house?

    _____ o'clock

7. In the park, Mrs Webber listens to the radio.
    What is happening on it?   _____

8. What does she buy from the newsagents? _____

9. Who does the bank manager call out to as he leaves his office?
    Is it   a) Marge   b) Edna   c) Hilary. _____

10. Where was the robber arrested?   _____

11. Who was he with?   _____

12. How many men were in the identity parade? _____

LISTEN UP!

Suspects

Name:_____   Date:_____

Mrs Webber's route

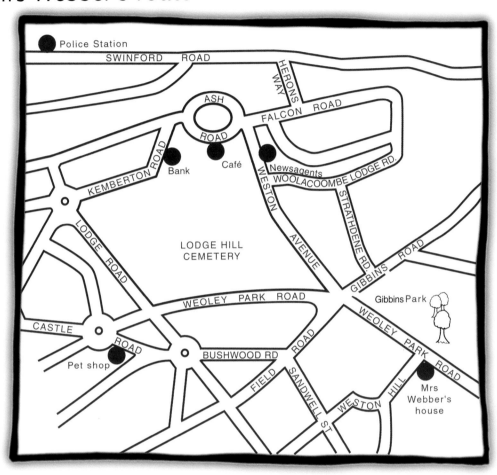

1. Mrs Webber left home at

2. She was in the park at

3. Mrs Webber was in the queue at the bank at

Suspects

Name:_____   Date:_____

Detective Inspector Spring describes where each of the robbers stand during the robbery. Listen again to the tape and mark on the CCTV image where each one is standing.

Write their dwarf names below:

1. _____   5. _____

2. _____   6. _____

3. _____   7. _____

4. _____

LISTEN UP!

Name:_____   Date:_____

- ## Headline 1
Use no more than five words for the local paper headline

THE HERALD

_____

- ## Diary entry
On a separate sheet of paper write what the bank manager might have put in his diary that night. Use these sentence starters to help you...

Tuesday

Today started out like any
other day but as

When the robbers rushed in

When it was all over

If only

- Give directions to Mrs Webber's house from the police station (use the map to help you).

The fall on Franwell Moor

Jackie: Dad, Dad! Wait for me. Not so fast.

Listen Up! guide: Oh dear, this is hard work as we're halfway up a hill. Jackie is feeling very tired after all this hiking. Her dad's a really fast walker and she does find it difficult to keep up. I tell you what, let's go and follow them as I think something is about to happen. Something that could be dangerous, and you are going to have to listen very hard to be able to help Jackie get out of a mess. So, let's go and hear how we can help…

Dad: Come on Jackie, just over this stile then one last hill and we should be able to see a village to the west of us. There's bound to be a bit of level ground where we can pitch our tent.

Jackie: Can't we rest for a bit Dad?

Dad: No time love, look the sun's starting to dip – can't risk it.

Jackie: But we've been walking for hours Dad, couldn't we just…

Dad: What did I say Ja…

Jackie: Dad watch out where you're…

Dad: Aaghh!

Jackie: Dad, Dad!!! Oh what should I do? OK, first check for a pulse, make sure his heart is still beating. I shouldn't move his head in case his neck is broken… I'll just check that he's breathing.
OK – seems to be. Oh Dad. The whistle, I should blow it in case there are any people close by.
Oh nobody is going to come. Where's the map? Yes there's a village, now what did Dad say about it?

Dad: Come on Jackie, just over this stile, then one last hill and we should be able to see a village to the west of us.

Jackie: But which way is west? How can I tell? Oh, if I had a compass I would know, but… oh yes there is another way. The sun rises in the east and sets in the west – and there's the sun dipping over there, so that direction must be the west. I must hurry.
Oh wait. How will I find my way back to this spot from the village? I must mark this route.
But what with? The tent pegs – I'll stick them in the ground to mark the way back to Dad.
There, there ahead – there's the village. And there's a woman – excuse me, excuse me!

Mrs Bell: And who would you be shouting at young lady? The name is Mrs Bell if you please.

Jackie: I'm sorry Mrs Bell. Is there a doctor here?

Mrs Bell: A doctor, in this house?

Jackie: No in the village, anywhere nearby – it's urgent.

Mrs Bell: A doctor in the village? Of course we've got a doctor, we've got all mod cons, we're not behind the times here. I have an inside toilet I'll have you know.

Jackie: Where? No, not the toilet, the doctor. My father's been hurt. I need to get medical help.

Mrs Bell: Oh well – then you should stop chatting and get going. You go up to the junction and turn left into Pennywhistle Lane, then second right into Thackeray Avenue and straight on to the traffic lights. Turn right at the lights, into Main Street with the post office at the end, I was only there myself this afternoon, picking up my pension. Turn right there into Blandings Road and the doctor is at number 12. Doctor Buxton.

Jackie: Thank you. Now, up to the junction and then what… Oh yes, turn left into… Pennywhistle Lane. Here we are. Oh Dad I'm almost there – be all right. Please! And then I take the… second right, that's it and turn into… Thackeray Avenue. Then straight ahead will be the… traffic lights, turn right. Yes, there's the post office and now I turn… left. Into… oh no that's wrong it was a right into… Blandings Road and the Doctor will be at… number 12. Here it is.
Doctor Buxton, Doctor Buxton!

Dr Buxton: Now then, where's the fire?

Jackie: It's my father, he's fallen and knocked himself out. We were hillwalking on Franwell Moor. Please, he needs help and it's getting dark.

Dr Buxton: I'll get my coat and bag. Dorothy, will you ring for an ambulance please? Tell them to meet us on Franwell Moor. What's your name lass?

Jackie: Jackie. Please hurry.

Dr Buxton: All right, where is he?

Jackie: Oh, what did that woman say?

Listen Up! guide: Well, Jackie has done really well so far to get to the doctor hasn't she? Now she has to guide the doctor back to her father. Can you remember the way? I'll remind you about the directions from Mrs Bell's to the doctor's – you could trace the route on the map (activity sheet 4a). The first thing you need to do is decide which is Mrs Bell's house, and which is the doctor's house, and label them. You could also label the post office and write in the missing street names. Now, draw in the compass points.
You could put on some other landmarks which might help you to give detailed directions – what could these be? Then you need to reverse the directions to get Jackie and the doctor back to the moor and Jackie's dad.
Listen again to Mrs Bell's directions:

Mrs Bell: You go up to the junction and turn left into Pennywhistle Lane, then second right into Thackeray Avenue and straight on to the traffic lights. Turn right at the lights, into Main Street with the post office at the end. Turn right there into Blandings Road and the doctor is at number 12. Doctor Buxton.

OK, so now use the map and your marked route to help you reverse the directions and get Jackie back to her dad on the moor. Read out your directions to a partner and check that they work. Write them down and compare them with Jackie's own.

The fall on Franwell Moor   Teacher's script

Jackie: Right doctor, so we turn, oh what way am I facing? Out into the road and I turned right into it so now I go left into Blandings Road. And here at the post office I turn… left into… Thackeray Avenue. And now I turn… left into… Pennywhistle Street and there is…

Dr Buxton: Mrs Bell.

Mrs Bell: Dr Buxton, you might want to pop in and have a look at my poor old feet.

Dr Buxton: Another time Mrs Bell, I've got a bit of an emergency. Now Jackie, here's the end of the village, which way do we go?

Jackie: Well we go… east. But the sun's gone behind the horizon now.

Dr Buxton: Don't worry lass, I've got a compass. Let's go.

Jackie: And there, there I can just see the tent peg – that way.

Dr Buxton: And another.

Jackie: That's the last one and there… there's my father.

Dr Buxton: Still out cold, but his pulse is strong. I'll cover him with my coat to keep him warm, we don't want his temperature to drop now that the sun's gone down. Now, where's that ambulance? I've got some flares in my bag so that we can attract the driver's attention and guide him to us.

Jackie: Will Dad be all right?

Dr Buxton: Thanks to you he will.

Listen Up! guide: And you'll be glad to know that Jackie's father was back to normal after a couple of days' rest and they finished their holiday and had a great time.

So, let's see how hard you were listening as I ask you some questions about Jackie's adventure. You can read along with them on activity sheet 4b. Let's go.

1. Why couldn't Jackie and her dad stop for a rest?

2. What three things did Jackie do after her father had fallen?

3. When Jackie's father fell, she went to get help from the village to the west. How did she know which way was west?

4. How does Jackie mark the route back to her father?

5. What mod con (oh, and that's short for modern convenience by the way) was Mrs Bell most proud of in her house?

6. What door number and street name did the doctor live at?

7. What did the doctor take with him to treat Jackie's dad?

8. What did Mrs Bell want to see the doctor about?

9. Without the sun to guide them, how did Jackie and the doctor know which direction to take on the moor?

10. What did the doctor have with him to attract the ambulance driver to the right spot?

The next five questions are a bit more difficult, but have a go. The answers are in the passage, but you have to do a bit of thinking to work them out. For example, the first one asks about the weather – Jackie and her dad don't actually mention what the weather is like, but you can get an idea from the sound effects and something that the doctor says near to the end. It might help you to listen to the questions, listen to the passage again, then

have a go at answering them.

11. What can you say about the weather?

12. What time would it be do you think, when Jackie and her dad reached the stile, if they were walking in a) late June, b) early October?

13. What sort of farming is there around the village?

14. What impression did you get about the size of the village, the amount of traffic and so on?

15. What sort of house do you think Mrs Bell lives in?

The next set of questions need you to empathise with the characters and use your common sense and logic. You'll find these on activity sheet 4c. It may help you to discuss them with another person, or in a group – be ready to say why you think as you do.

16. How was Jackie feeling at the beginning of the passage? Write what she might have been thinking in the thought bubble.

17. What did this experience teach Jackie about being prepared for the worst? What do you think she might have put in her rucksack next time she went walking?

18. What could Jackie have done if there had been no doctor in the village?

19. Who is Dorothy?

20. The doctor's surgery and the post office are mentioned in the passage – what other amenities do you think would be essential in a small village which is a) two miles from the nearest town, b) twenty miles from the nearest town?

So, how did you do on those – some of those were difficult weren't they? And did you split up into pairs or into a group to talk about the characters?

Now I definitely want you to find a partner as we are going to do some acting. One of you will play Jackie, the other her dad. This is the scene I want you to enact:

Jackie was never very keen on going walking in the first place; after this experience she is even less enthusiastic. But her dad loves walking on the moors and a few weeks later, he tries to persuade Jackie to go on another expedition with him. What could he say or offer to do to encourage Jackie to go along?

With your partner, work out what each character might say in the discussion. You could try playing both parts and see what comes up.

Well that's it. I'm so glad everything ended well for Jackie. How about you, did you do well on the questions, and the acting? I hope so, I hope you are listening harder and harder now. Right, I shall say goodbye, you'll be hearing from me!

LISTEN UP!

The fall on Franwell Moor   Activity sheet 4a

Name:_____   Date:_____

Franwell Moor

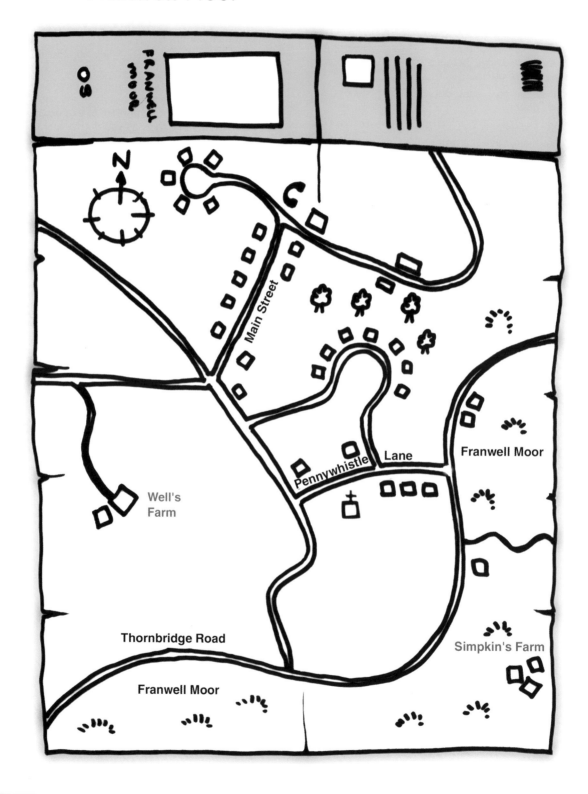

LISTEN UP!

The fall on Franwell Moor   Activity sheet 4b

Name:_____   Date:_____

1. Why couldn't Jackie and her dad stop for a rest?
    _____

2. What three things did Jackie do after her father had fallen?
    _____
    _____

3. When Jackie's father fell, she went to get help from the village
    to the west. How did she know which way was west?
    _____

4. How does Jackie mark the route back to her father?
    _____

5. What mod con was Mrs Bell most proud of in her house?
    _____

6. What door number and street name did the doctor live at?
    _____

7. What did the doctor take with him to treat Jackie's dad?
    _____

8. What did Mrs Bell want to see the doctor about?
    _____

9. Without the sun to guide them, how did Jackie and the
    doctor know which direction to take on the moor?
    _____

10. What did the doctor have with him to attract the ambulance
    driver to the right spot? _____

11. What can you say about the weather?
    _____

12. What time would it be do you think, when Jackie and her
    dad reached the stile, if they were walking in
    a) late June _____ b) early October _____

13. What sort of farming is there around the village?
    _____

14. What impression did you get about the size of the village,
    the amount of traffic and so on? _____
    _____

15. What sort of house do you think Mrs Bell lives in?
    _____

LISTEN UP!

The fall on Franwell Moor Activity sheet 4c

Name:_____ Date:_____

16. How was Jackie feeling at the beginning of the passage? Write what she might have been thinking in the thought bubble.

17. What did this experience teach Jackie about being prepared for the worst? What do you think she might have put in her rucksack next time she went walking? _____

_____

_____

18. What could Jackie have done if there had been no doctor in the village? _____

_____

_____

19. Who is Dorothy? _____

20. The doctor's surgery and the post office are mentioned in the passage. What other amenities do you think would be essential in a small village which is

a) two miles from the nearest town,   b) twenty miles from the nearest town?

_____   _____

_____   _____

_____   _____

_____   _____

21. Role play:

Jackie was never very keen on going walking in the first place; after this experience she is even less enthusiastic. But her dad loves walking on the moors and a few weeks later, he tries to persuade Jackie to go on another expedition with him. What could he say or offer to do to encourage Jackie to go along? With your partner, work out what each character might say in the discussion.

LISTEN UP!

The fall on Franwell Moor   Activity sheet 4d

Name:_____   Date:_____

Memory skills

Here is a list of some of the things you might take with you on an overnight trek on the moors.

Read the list carefully and test each other on how many items you can remember.

Are there any tricks you can use to help you? You could try:

- visualising the items set out on your bed at home, or the kitchen table.

- grouping them into sets of three or four, for example 'medical supplies' together.

- grouping them alphabetically.

1. tent
2. stove
3. chocolate
4. antiseptic cream
5. map
5. bandage
7. paracetemol
8. extra sweater
9. penknife
10. cooking pan

11. water
12. sleeping bag
13. compass
14. baked beans
15. sausages
16. whistle
17. clean socks
18. matches
19. spoon and fork
20. torch

• If you ran out of space in your rucksack and had to leave out five items, which would you leave behind?

_____   _____
_____   _____
_____

Shopping

Listen Up! guide: Hello there. Well we're travelling – but on what? Can you hear any clues?
We're heading into town – to go shopping. I love to shop, do you? Anyway, we have to help Jack and his mum shop, and you have to listen to what happens so you can answer my questions at the end. OK, open your ears and let's go shopping…

Mother: Come on Jack, this is our stop, ring the bell.

Jack: But the game shop is in Tolliver Street, that's at the other end of the high street.

Mother: We are not getting your game first. We have to get you some new jeans, a present for your dad and didn't you say you had to have some project folders to take into school?

Jack: But that's boring.

Mother: And necessary.

Jack: But it makes sense to go right to the end of the high street and work our way back from there, that way the ride back is shorter.

Mother: That's true, but if you get the game first you'll want to play it all afternoon and won't want to be bothered with the other stuff – this way you only get it if you behave.

Jack: Blackmail. That's not fair – I am buying it with my own money after all. I've got erm…

Mother: Let's sort that out when we get off.

Jack: Well, I've got two ten pound notes, one five pound note, twelve one pound coins and 97 pence in change.

Mother: And how much is the game?

Jack: £39.99

Mother: Well, you can't afford it then.

Jack: Well how much have I got?

Mother: You work it out – come on. Two ten pounds, one five pound note, twelve one pound coins and 97 pence in change.

Jack: Oh mum…

Listen Up! guide: Before Jack and his mother go inside the store, can you work out how much money Jack has? Write down what he said and total it up.

Jack: Well, I've got two ten pound notes, one five pound note, twelve one pound coins and 97 pence in change.

Mother: My son the human calculator. Look, here's Patterson's Department store. In we go. Where's the store guide? There it is.

Jack: The boys' department is on floor two. That's where bedding is and soft furnishings.

Mother: And school supplies are in the basement, with books and office equipment.

Jack: I was thinking of getting dad a tie.

Mother: That's nice.

Jack: One that's shaped like a fish – a shark maybe.

Mother: Mmm! Well, menswear is on the first floor. With sports equipment and the cafeteria.

Jack: Let's split up – we can get this done quicker that way.

Mother: Oh no, I'm not trusting you to buy anything by yourself. Let's get the lift.
Well that wasn't too bad. Those jeans were a real bargain, and the missing button isn't a problem – I'll soon find a replacement in my button jar at home. I'm not sure about those project folders though – are you certain it's OK to have South Park characters all over them?

Jack: Of course it is Mum – all the other kids have got the same sort of stuff – the Simpsons or South Park, or the girls have ones with their favourite pop stars on. The teachers don't mind – Miss Potter has got one for her lesson plans with Robbie Williams on it so she can't complain! I still haven't got anything for Dad.

Mother: Well, I didn't think those ties were suitable. What else could you get him?

Jack: I think he'd like a Gameboy.

Mother: No he would not! He might like a screwdriver set.

Jack: Well, where would I get that?

Mother: A hardware shop. There's one just across the street, let's cross over.

Jack: How much do I get to spend on him?

Mother: What do you mean how much? I gave you ten pounds yesterday.

Jack: But that's included in the money to buy my game.

Mother: Oh no it isn't. That was for you to buy a present for your father.

Jack: Oh!

Mother: Come on, let's get a screwdriver set for your dad. That was good, only £6.50.

Jack: Yes, but I'm still short of money for my game.

Mother: Well, as you can't buy the game we might as well go home.

Jack: Oh no, let me at least go and look around the shop.

Mother: Look there's the game shop, and there's a poster in the window.

Jack: What does it say?

Mother: One day only – sale. 30% discount on all purchases.

Jack: 30% off my game – so how much is it now?

Mother: Well without discount, the game costs £39.99, so the way I do it in my head is to work out 10% first. That's easy because you just move the decimal point. 10% of £39.99 is £3.99. But there is 30% off – that's three times as much, three times £3.99. So now you can work it out – see what 3 times £3.99 comes to then take that sum away from £39.99.

Jack: I can afford my game now then, at least I think I can. Will you check it for me mum?

Mother: I think you might even have some left over to buy your dad a birthday card…

Listen Up! guide: Well, let's hope Jack enjoys his game and how well did you do calculating the money he needed to buy it?

Now, I'm going to ask you some questions to find out how hard you were listening, so let's go. You can read along with them on activity sheet 5a.

1. How were Jack and his mum travelling to town? By a) car b) train or c) bus?

2. Where did Jack want to go first? a) McDonald's b) the game shop or c) the department store?

3a. Where is the game shop?

a) in Tolliver Street b) High Street or c) Boliver Street?

3b. What does his mum want to get first?
Choose three things from:

• school blazer

• new shoes

• jeans

• sports kit

• folders

• Dad's birthday present

4. What is the name of the department store?
a) Madison's b) Debenham's or c) Patterson's?

5. How much money has Jack got? Add together two ten pound notes, one five pound note, twelve pound coins and ninety seven pence in change.

6. What does Jack want to buy for his dad's birthday present? a) golf balls b) a tie or c) new socks?

7. What does he actually buy in the end?
a) a sports bag b) a screwdriver set or c) a CD?

8. Why were Jack's jeans at a bargain price?
a) because they were last year's stock b) one trouser leg was longer than the other or c) there was a button missing?

9. What sort of project folders did he get? a) plain blue b) pop-star designs or c) South Park?

Did Jack really have enough money for his game? Use the working out sheet (activity sheet 5b) to decide whether or not he had enough left over to buy his dad a birthday card.

Well, that's that. Jack and his mother are happy and I hope you are too because you did so well answering my questions. Remember, keep your ears open and listen up! You'll be hearing from me.

Name:_____   Date:_____

Put a ring around the right answer.

1. How were Jack and his mum travelling to town?
   By   a) car   b) train   or c) bus?

2. Where did Jack want to go first?
   a) McDonald's b) the game shop or c) the department store?

3a. Where is the game shop?
   a) in Tolliver Street   b) High Street   or c) Boliver Street?

3b. What does his mum want to get first?
   Choose three things from:

   school blazer   sports kit   jeans

   new shoes   folders   Dad's birthday present

4. What is the name of the department store?
   a) Madison's   b) Debenham's   or c) Patterson's?

5. How much money has Jack got?   £   p
   Add together two ten pound notes,
   one five pound note,
   twelve pound coins
   and ninety seven pence in change:

6. What does Jack want to buy for his dad's birthday present?
   a) golf balls   b) a tie   or c) new socks?

7. What does he actually buy in the end?
   a) a sports bag   b) a screwdriver set   or c) a CD?

8. Why were Jack's jeans a bargain price?
   a) because they were last year's stock
   b) one trouser leg was longer than the other or
   c) there was a button missing?

9. What sort of project folders did he get?
   a) plain blue   b) pop-star designs   or c) South Park?

LISTEN UP!

Shopping

Name:_____   Date:_____

How much money did Jack have left?

£ . p	
	a

This is how much money Jack had to start with :
He spent £6.50 on his dad's present: −
So that left him with:

The price of the game was £39.99, but with 30% off.
Work out 30% like this:
10% of 39.99 is
So 30% is   3 x [   ] = [*]
So the game cost:

	39.99
−	*
=	b

Jack had this much to buy the game:
Subtract the cost of the game to find out   −
how much money he had left:

	a
	b
= £ . p	

Here is another one for you to try:

Jack's mum had £25 to spend on new jeans she had seen in the store. In the sale, the pair is reduced by 20%. (That's £25 take away 10% and another 10%.) How much does she pay? How much has she got left over?

With all the shopping finished, Jack and his mum go into a burger bar for something to eat. Jack has a Whopper burger and a cola, his mum has a Cheeseburger and a coffee. How much is the bill? How much change will there be from a ten pound note?

Menu:

Whopper	£1.85	Coffee	90p
Cheeseburger	£1.75	Tea	80p
Veggie-burger	£1.65	Milk shake	£1.00
Chicken bun	£1.90	Cola	85p
French fries	95p		

LISTEN UP!

Name:_____   Date:_____

Department store floor guide

Can you place the goods listed on the right floor?
(Not all of them are mentioned in the recording – use your own judgement to decide where these might be...)

Menswear   Ladieswear   Boyswear
Customer toilets   Girlswear   Electrical goods
Cafeteria   Soft Furnishings   Carpets
Furniture   Bedding   Sports equipment
Office and school supplies

3 — Third Floor

2 — Second Floor

1 — First Floor

G — Ground Floor

B — Basement

LISTEN UP!

Shopping

Name:_____   Date:_____

Department stores and supermarkets sell lots of different things but there are still smaller, specialist shops around, like the hardware shop where Jack bought the screwdriver set.

Match the items to the shops where you could buy them.

Tom's Bakery	apples, carrots
Jefferson's Greengrocers	a gold chain, a watch
Buxton's Men's Tailoring	cod, halibut
Hoar Cross Butchers	a food mixer, a vacuum cleaner
High Street Off-licence	CDs and tapes
Jenny's Florist	a pushchair, a cot
Pharmacy	apple turnovers, custard tarts
Redhill Delicatessen	a suit, shirts
DIY shop	a vase, a travel bag
Babyland	stamps, special delivery labels
Toys 4 Us	daffodil bulbs, potting compost
Newsagent	tennis racquet, jogging shoes
Post Office	wallpaper, paintbrushes
Garden Centre	special cured ham, olives
Sports Emporium	beer, wine
Music Megastore	lamb chops, steak
Jewellers	a bouquet of flowers
Gifts Galore	medicine, tablets
Everything Electric	a playhouse, silver scooter
Fresh from the Sea	magazines, comics

Shopping

Name:_____ Date:_____

Planning a High Street

There are lots of things to think about when planning a new High Street.
In Bridgetown the old High Street has been demolished to make way for a new
ring road and the developers are thinking about which shops and services should
be on the town's High Street and which would be better at the out-of-town
retail park. They also have to think about things like bus stops, litter bins and
benches. There are all sorts of people in Bridgetown – youngsters, mothers with
babies, business people and elderly pensioners who have to rely on buses. They
all have to be catered for. The next town is much bigger than Bridgetown, but is
ten miles away.

Choose outlets from the list below, and place them on the High Street plan
(activity sheet 5f). Decide which outlets would be better at the retail park, and
which shouldn't be given planning permission at all – be ready to explain your
decisions. Remember to draw in the bus stops (x4), benches (x4), pedestrian
crossings (x2) and litter bins (x6).

1. National bank
2. Building society
3. Babyland
4. Hoar Cross Butchers
5. Pharmacy
6. Sports Emporium
7. Newsagents
8. Post Office
9. Discount Carpets
10. Fish and chip shop
11. Abigail's – ladies clothes
12. Fresh from the Sea
13. The Dog and Duck – pub
14. Playmaster – multi-screen cinema, bingo and tenpin bowling
15. Furniture World
16. Public toilets
17. Sameday supermarket
18. Everything Electric
19. Doctor's surgery
20. Music Megastore
21. DIY Superstore
22. INCA – electrical warehouse
23. Jenny's Florist
24. Jewellers
25. Hunter's Family Clothing
26. Redhill Delicatessen
27. Library

LISTEN UP!

Name:_____   Date:_____

**2 miles to
High Bridge
retail park**

HIGH STREET

1
2
3
4
5
6
7
8
9
10
11
12
13
14
15
16
17
18
19

Teacher's notes: Activities 6–20

The fifteen shorter, scripted activities can be read out in 'real time' by the teacher or AOT, or recorded onto tape. (Using a taped script frees you up to observe pupils, help them out when necessary and assess their skills during the activity.)
A familiar voice will be advantageous to many pupils – particularly those with special needs. It should be made clear to pupils that the instructions will be read out only once and not repeated, to ensure their full attention. (The teacher will of course, amend this as required to suit the ability of the pupils, but frequent repetition will make the activity tedious for those pupils who have attended well.)

LISTEN UP!

Class portraits

Miss Merton, the new teacher, asked everyone in the class to draw a self-portrait. They also wrote descriptions of themselves. But they weren't very good at drawing! When Miss Merton took the pictures home she couldn't work out who was who.

Listen to her pupils' descriptions. Write the correct names by the portraits, or draw lines to link the pictures with the names printed down the side of the sheet.

Sam wrote: I am a boy and I have dark hair, which is short and curly. I knocked out my two front teeth when I fell off my bike.

Carly wrote: I am a girl. My hair is blonde and I have it long with a short fringe. I wear glasses.

Tom wrote: I am a boy with short, straight dark hair. I wear an earring in my left ear.

Lottie wrote: I am a girl with short, dark wavy hair. I have a beauty spot on my right cheek.

Ben wrote: I am a boy. I have very short fair hair. There are freckles on my nose, and my mum says I have a cheeky grin.

Amy wrote: I am a girl. My hair is fair and it reaches down to my shoulders. I usually wear it in a hairband.

Mark wrote: I am Sam's twin brother, but I still have all my teeth.

Jodie wrote: I am a girl with long fair hair, which I wear in bunches. I have freckles and I wear earrings.

Name:_____   Date:_____

Sam

Carly

Tom

Lottie

Ben

Amy

Mark

Jodie

Bags it's mine

On a flight back from Spain, eight people had identical bags. When they came to pick their luggage from the carousel, they couldn't tell which bag was which.

The lost property officer opened all the bags and called out what was in them.

Listen to the contents of the bags. Four items are listed for each.
On the pictures, only two items are shown in each bag.
For each person, identify the correct bag and draw in the missing items.
Draw lines to link the bags with the correct luggage labels.

1. Mrs Patel   A paint box, a sketchbook, a folding stool and a bag of sweets.

2. Lizzie   A book, a sketchbook, pencils and a bag of sweets.

3. Tim   A camera, a mobile phone, a bag of sweets and a sketchbook.

4. Dilip   A Gameboy, some marbles, a bar of chocolate and some felt pens.

5. Mr Smith   A fishing rod, a folding stool, a book and a mobile phone.

6. Emma   A Gameboy, a bag of sweets, a book and some felt pens.

7. Jack   A Walkman, some cassettes, a book and a bar of chocolate.

8. Miss Hassan   A camera, a book, a bar of chocolate and a sketchbook.

Extension
Work in a group.
Each person draws four items they would pack in their bag, without showing the others.
Collect up all the drawings and shuffle them.
Describe the contents of each bag in turn.
Either invite the group to guess whose bag it is, or ask the pupils to identify their own bags from the description.

LISTEN UP!

Bags it's mine

Name:_____ Date:_____

Mrs Patel • Lizzie • Tim • Dilip • Mr Smith • Emma • Jack • Miss Hassan

Caught speeding!

The police have a list of the registration numbers of cars caught by a speed camera in a 30 mile per hour zone.

Listen and fill in the registration numbers on the car number plates.

1.   Car number 1:   X585 SGP
2.   Car number 2:   R72 PAT
3.   Car number 3:   Y291 ULVP
4.   Car number 4:   S422 TRD
5.   Car number 5:   F329 PDG
6.   Car number 6:   EZA 645Y
7.   Car number 7:   DLJ 524T
8.   Car number 8:   L628 ALM

Listen to these instructions and fill in the speed each car was doing.

9.   The car whose numbers add to 16 was doing 35 miles per hour.
10.   The car whose numbers add to 15 was doing 42 miles per hour.
11.   The car whose numbers add to 12 was doing 56 miles per hour.
12.   The car whose numbers add to 9 was doing 38 miles per hour.
13.   The car whose numbers add to 8 was doing 40 miles per hour.
14.   The car whose numbers add to 11 was doing 44 miles per hour.
15.   The car whose numbers add to 14 was doing 42 miles per hour.
16.   The car whose numbers add to 18 was doing 52 miles per hour.

LISTEN UP!

Caught speeding!

Name:_____   Date:_____

Car number 1

Speed: _____ miles per hour

Car number 2

Speed: _____ miles per hour

Car number 3

Speed: _____ miles per hour

Car number 4

Speed: _____ miles per hour

Car number 5

Speed: _____ miles per hour

Car number 6

Speed: _____ miles per hour

Car number 7

Speed: _____ miles per hour

Car number 8

Speed: _____ miles per hour

LISTEN UP!

Skateboard mix-up

After practising on the ramp, the skateboarding team have a break to discuss tactics.

They leave their skateboards in a pile at the side of the ramp.

When it's time to practise again it takes them ages to find their own skateboards.

Follow these instructions to match the skateboards to their owners.
Draw lines to match the names to the correct skateboards.

1. Ali's skateboard has zigzags and circles.
2. Kim's skateboard has circles, triangles and squares.
3. Sam's skateboard has triangles, squares and diamonds.
4. Martin's skateboard has triangles and squares.
5. Lucy's skateboard has zigzags, squares and circles.
6. Zac's skateboard has squares and rectangles.
7. Carl's skateboard has squares and zigzags.
8. Beth's skateboard has zigzags, circles and triangles.
9. Rick's skateboard has triangles, squares, circles and dots.
10. Deepal's skateboard has circles and diamonds.
11. Helen's skateboard has squares, triangles and zigzags.
12. Jamila's skateboard has circles, zigzags and diamonds.

Extension
- Colour in the skateboards using these colours:
  Zigzags: red
  Triangles: blue
  Squares: yellow
  Rectangles: green
  Circles: black
  Diamonds: orange
- Design a skateboard using five different shapes.

LISTEN UP!

Skateboard mix-up

Name:_____   Date:_____

Ali

Lucy

Rick

Kim

Zac

Helen

Sam

Carl

Deepal

Martin

Beth

Jamila

Flags

Colour the flags according to the instructions.

1. Find the flag with the leaf.
   Colour the leaf red.
   Colour the two outside stripes red.
   Leave the stripe around the leaf white.

2. Find the flag with the circle in the middle.
   Colour the circle red.
   Leave the rest white.

3. Find the flag on the top right-hand corner of the sheet.
   Colour the left-hand stripe black.
   Colour the centre stripe yellow.
   Colour the right-hand stripe red.

4. Find the flag with the crosses right across it.
   Colour all the triangles blue.
   Colour the insides of the diagonal lines red, leaving white sections on either side.
   Colour the insides of the vertical and horizontal lines red, leaving white sections on either side.

5. Find the flag with one cross in the middle.
   Colour the flag red, leaving the cross white.

6. Find the flag in the bottom left-hand corner of the sheet.
   Colour the left-hand stripe green.
   Leave the centre stripe white.
   Colour the right-hand stripe red.

7. Find the flag in the bottom right-hand corner of the sheet.
   Colour the top stripe red.
   Leave the middle stripe white.
   Colour the bottom stripe blue.

8. Find the flag that is left with three vertical stripes.
   Colour the left-hand stripe blue.
   Leave the middle stripe white.
   Colour the right-hand stripe red.

9. Find the flag with the crescent and star.
   Leave the left-hand stripe white.

Colour the rest of the flag green, leaving the crescent and star white.

10. The last flag has three horizontal stripes.
    Colour the top stripe black.
    Colour the middle stripe red.
    Colour the bottom stripe yellow.

Listen to the instructions and match the flags to the names of the countries written down the middle of the sheet.

Pakistan: the flag has a white stripe down the left-hand side, and a white crescent and star on a green background.

Canada: the flag has two red stripes outside a white stripe, with a red maple leaf in it.

Germany: the flag has three horizontal stripes. Starting at the top they are black, red and yellow.

Belgium: the flag has three vertical stripes. From left to right they are black, yellow and red.

Japan: the flag is white with a red circle in it.

Italy: the flag has three vertical stripes. From right to left they are red, white and green.

The Netherlands: the flag has three horizontal stripes. Starting at the bottom they are blue, white and red.

Great Britain: the flag has one diagonal cross and one cross with vertical and horizontal lines, on a blue background. Each cross contains one red cross within a white cross.

Extension

There are two flags left.
Find out which countries they are from.

LISTEN UP!

Flags

Name:_____   Date:_____

Pakistan

Canada

Germany

Belgium

Japan

Italy

The Netherlands

Great Britain

Pizza party

It is Saleem's birthday and he is having a party at a pizza restaurant.

Listen to the instructions and work out where everyone is sitting.

Draw lines to link the names to the pizzas.

1. Saleem has been busy opening his presents, so he has eaten less pizza than everyone else.

2. Amy ordered a side salad with her pizza. So far she has eaten two slices of her pizza.

3. Fred has eaten half his pizza. He has ordered a side salad as well.

4. Bina is sitting opposite Amy. She has ordered a side salad.
   She has three slices of pizza left. Draw them on her plate.

5. Jade has half her pizza left.

6. Lyn has 5 slices of pizza left. She also has a side salad.

7. Mark is sitting between Bina and Jade.
   He has eaten 3 slices of pizza.
   He has also ordered a side salad. Draw this by his plate.

8. Nick is sitting opposite Mark.
   He has eaten 6 slices of pizza.
   How many does he have left? Draw them on his plate.

9. The waiter brings over a tray of drinks.
   Draw the drinks by the right plates. Use the correct colours.
   Nick and Bina have cola.
   Fred and Mark have cherryade.
   Amy has lime cordial.
   Saleem and Jade have orange juice.
   The last drink is pineapple juice.

Extension

How many slices of pizza are left on the plates altogether?

How many slices have been eaten?

LISTEN UP!

Name:_____   Date:_____

Saleem

Mark

Fred

Nick

Jade

Bina

Amy

Lyn

The race

The horses and jockeys for the 2.30 race are waiting in the paddock.

The horses need to be given their numbers.

Follow these instructions to write their numbers in the circles and get the riders ready.

1. Jockey number 1's horse is still eating its lunch.
   The jockey is chewing bubble gum. Draw the bubble she blows.
2. Jockey number 2's horse has leg bandages on its front legs.
   The jockey has forgotten his boots. Draw them on.
3. Jockey number 3's horse has a bad eye.
   The jockey has forgotten her glasses. Draw them on for her.
4. Jockey number 4's horse has bandages on all four legs.
   The jockey has a bad wrist. Draw on his bandage.
5. Jockey number 5's horse is embarassed by the plaits in her mane.
   Draw plaits for the jockey too.
6. Jockey number 6's horse has lost a shoe.
   The jockey has no hat. Draw one on for him.

Extension

Listen to the race commentary and answer the questions.
(It might help you to draw a cross next to each horse as it leaves the race.)

And they're off! Number 3 takes the lead, followed by number 1 in second place. As they come round the first bend, number 1 stops to eat some long grass by the track! Number 5 is catching up; number 3 is still in the lead. And they come to the first fence. But number 3 hasn't seen it and runs straight into it. She's out of the race!

- Who is in the lead now?
- Who else is left in the race?
- Who has dropped out?

Now it's number 5 still in the lead, closely followed by numbers 2, 4 and 6. But number 6 is limping badly with a lost shoe, and has given up. As number 5 jumps the next fence the photographers' cameras flash – and she's gone all shy! Number 5 is galloping back to the start! So number 2 is in the lead, with only 100 metres left to go.

- Who else is still in the race?

So it's number 2 and number 4 coming up to the finish. It's very close – neck and neck – and there's the winner – he's made it in spite of his jockey's bad wrist!

- Who won the race?

Name:_____   Date:_____

White elephant stall

Gemma and Lucy are running the white elephant stall at the school fête.

Follow the instructions to help them price the items on the stall.
Write the prices on the labels as they are given.

1. The book is 15 pence.
2. The candle is £1.
3. The white elephant is half the price of the candle.
4. The teddy bear is the same price as the candle.
5. The jam is 15 pence cheaper than the teddy bear.

Once the sale starts, things sell quickly.
Follow the instructions to work out what these people buy.

6. Steve buys a present each for his two brothers. He spends exactly £1.05.
   Write an S on the two things he buys.

7. Deepak has emptied his piggy bank and has 3 five pence pieces and 2 twenty pence pieces. He spends it all on a present for his Granny.
   Write a D on the thing he buys.

8. Jade has a five pound note. She buys one thing from the stall and gets £4.10 change.
   Write a J on the thing she buys.

9. Karl spends £1.50 on a present for his mum and one for his dad.
   Write a K on the things he buys.

10. Roger has spent most of his money on the tombola and hasn't won anything. He has 6 twenty pence pieces left, but he has to save 60 pence for his bus fare home.
    He spends all his remaining money on one thing.
    Write an R on the thing he buys.

11. Alix has 75 pence. She buys presents for her three brothers and spends the same amount of money on each of them.
    Write an A on the things she buys.

12. Mina had £2. She bought some things on the food stall: a cake for 60 pence, a biscuit for 30 pence, some crisps for 25 pence and some apple juice for 40 pence. She spent the rest of her money on a present for her mother. Write an M on the thing she buys.

Extension

1. Colour red anything that costs more than 75 pence.
2. Colour yellow anything that costs more than 50 pence but less than 75 pence.
3. Colour blue anything that costs more than 25 pence but less than 50 pence.
4. Colour green anything that costs less than 25 pence.

White elephant stall   Activity sheet 13

Name:_____   Date:_____

90p

25p

25p

45p

75p

25p

80p

70p

60p

55p

55p

Nail art

Hannah has been experimenting with nail art.
Decorate her nails following these instructions.

1. Hannah has painted her two thumb nails green.

2. On her right thumb nail she has stuck a black diamond shape.

3. On her left thumb nail she has stuck a black circle shape.

4. On Hannah's right hand, the index finger and little finger have pale pink nails.

5. On the index finger nail there is a red zigzag sticker.

6. Hannah has pierced the top of the nail on the little finger and put a small ring through it.

7. On Hannah's left hand, the index finger and the ring finger nails are purple.

8. On the ring finger nail Hannah has a small sticker of a letter H.

9. The middle finger nails of both hands are blue. The right one has a smiley face sticker on it, and the left one has a grumpy face sticker.

10. The last nail on the right hand is orange.

11. The last nail on the left hand is yellow. It has a small red heart sticker on it.

Once Hannah had finished her nails she put some temporary tattoos on her hands.

12. On the back of her left hand she put her initial H.

13. On the back of her right hand she put a butterfly.

Extension

Draw around your own hands and then colour and decorate the nails.
Now draw round your hands again. Give the empty hands to your friend.
Describe the patterns and colours you have used for your friend to copy onto the empty hands.

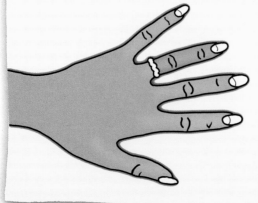

Nail art

Name:_____ Date:_____

Chocolate box

Here are the chocolates for a new chocolate selection box.
They are all wrapped in different ways.

Follow the instructions to draw on the wrappings.

1.　The circular chocolate is wrapped in purple paper with pink spots.

2.　Find the square chocolate. Draw two diagonal lines to divide the square into four triangles. Colour the top triangle blue. Then colour the remaining triangles red, green and yellow, going round the square clockwise.

3.　Find the chocolate in the shape of a hexagon. Divide it in half with a horizontal line across the middle. Colour the top half blue and the bottom half blue with red stripes.

4.　Find the chocolate shaped like a triangle. Draw a smaller triangle inside it. Colour the smaller triangle yellow. Colour the rest of the shape green.

5.　Find the oval-shaped chocolate. Draw a wide orange line down the middle of it, from top to bottom. Colour the left-hand part of the oval blue. Colour the right-hand part of the oval green.

6.　Find the chocolate shaped like a pentagon. Draw lines in from each corner to meet at the middle. Colour the top triangle red. Going round the pentagon anticlockwise, colour the other triangles yellow, blue, orange and green.

7.　Find the long thin rectangle chocolate. Divide it into quarters with horizontal lines. Colour the top one red, and the next one blue. Repeat the pattern for the next two sections.

8.　Find the diamond-shaped chocolate. Draw a vertical line between the top and bottom corners. Draw a horizontal line between the other two corners. Starting with the top left triangle, and going round clockwise, colour the sections orange, yellow, red and blue.

9.　The last chocolate is an octagon. Divide it into 8 triangles by joining opposite corners with straight lines. Colour the bottom triangle green. Then continue round the octagon colouring alternate triangles red and green.

Extension
Design the lid for the chocolate box.

LISTEN UP!

Chocolate box

Name:_____   Date:_____

Activity 16

What am I ?

Solve the riddles and number the
pictures according to the instructions.

1. I light your way in the dark. I run on batteries. Label me 1.

2. Sometimes I need sharpening. I am used for drawing and colouring. Label me 2.

3. I am worn on the head. Kings and queens wear me. Label me 3.

4. I am used for woodwork. I am made of metal and wood. I have teeth. Label me 4.

5. I float. I carry passengers and cargo across the sea. Label me 5.

6. I live in a field. The farmer milks me twice a day. Label me 6.

7. I flicker and melt when I burn. Label me 7.

8. I grow on a tree in a warm country. My name is the same as my colour. Label me 8.

9. I am used for woodwork. I am made of metal and wood. I bang in nails. Label me 9.

10. I live in a field but I sleep in a shed at night so the fox can't catch me. I lay an egg every day. Label me 10.

11. I am a toy. I float in the bath. Label me 11.

12. I light up a room. I have a bulb and a shade. Label me 12.

13. I grow on a tree. Squirrels eat me, but people do not. Label me 13.

14. I am used for drawing and colouring. If you use me too much I run out of ink. Label me 14.

15. I live in a field. My woolly coat keeps me warm. Label me 15.

16. I am worn on the head. The people that wear me put out fires. Label me 16.

17. I grow on a tree. I can be red or green. Label me 17.

Extension

18. You need me to light number 7. Label me 18.

19. You need me to sharpen number 2. Label me 19.

20. I hold the things you get from number 10. Label me 20.

21. Number 9 bangs me into pieces of wood. Label me 21.

22. You need me to make number 1 work. Label me 22.

23. Throw me overboard and I will hold number 5 still. Label me 23.

LISTEN UP!

What am I?

Name:_____   Date:_____

Join the dots

Follow the instructions to draw the numbered dots.

Make sure all your dots are at a point where two lines cross.

Don't join them up until you have drawn them all.

1.   Begin at the dot labelled 'Start'. Move 3 squares east. Draw a dot and label it 1.
2.   Move 3 squares north. Draw a dot and label it 2.
3.   Move 1 square east and 1 square north. Draw a dot and label it 3.
4.   Move 1 square east and 1 square south. Draw a dot and label it 4.
5.   Move 3 squares south. Draw a dot and label it 5.
6.   Move 3 squares east. Draw a dot and label it 6.
7.   Move 3 squares north. Draw a dot and label it 7.
8.   Move 1 square west. Draw a dot and label it 8.
9.   Move 9 squares north. Draw a dot and label it 9.
10.   Move 1 square east. Draw a dot and label it 10.
11.   Move 3 squares north. Draw a dot and label it 11.
12.   Move 1 square west. Draw a dot and label it 12.
13.   Move 1 square south. Draw a dot and label it 13.
14.   Move 1 square west. Draw a dot and label it 14.
15.   Move I square north. Draw a dot and label it 15.
16.   Move 2 squares west. Draw a dot and label it 16.
17.   Move 1 square south. Draw a dot and label it 17.
18.   Move 1 square west. Draw a dot and label it 18.
19.   Move 1 square north. Draw a dot and label it 19.
20.   Move 1 square west. Draw a dot and label it 20.
21.   Move 1 square south. Draw a dot and label it 21.
22.   Move 1 square west. Draw a dot and label it 22.
23.   Move 1 square north. Draw a dot and label it 23.
24.   Move 1 square west. Draw a dot and label it 24.
25.   Move 3 squares south. Draw a dot and label it 25.
26.   Move 1 square east. Draw a dot and label it 26.
27.   Move 9 squares south. Draw a dot and label it 27.
28.   Move 1 square west. Draw a dot and label it 28.

Now join all your dots in order.

Join the start to dot 1. Join dot 28 to the start.

What have you drawn?

Extension

Make up your own join the dots picture with instructions.

Name:_____   Date:_____

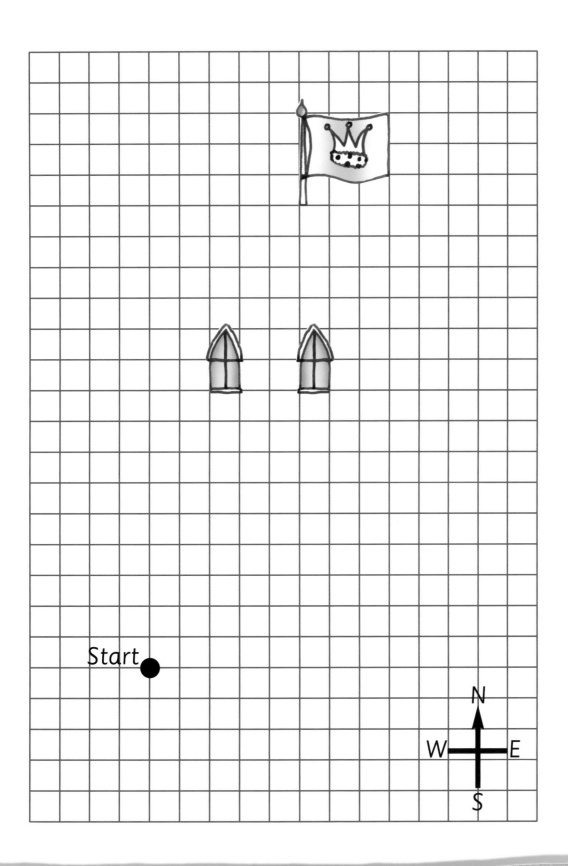

Activity 18

Prizes

In a TV game show, contestants watch prizes go past them on a conveyor belt. Afterwards they have one minute to tell the show's host which prizes they remember.

Four contestants won prizes on last week's show.
Listen to what they won. Then label their prizes with their initial.

1. Liam won a mobile phone, a paint box, a cuddly toy and a box of chocolates. Label these L.

2. Anna won a cutlery set, a doll, two cushions and a DVD player. Label these A.

3. Ben won a pot plant, a CD and tape player, a basketball set, a tea set and a computer. Label these B.

4. Samir won a TV, a lamp, some saucepans, a pair of trainers and a picture. Label these S.

5. Kerensa won the prizes that were left over. What were they?

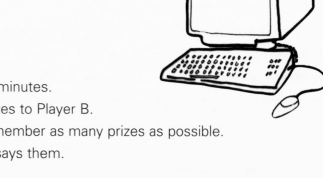

Extension
Work in pairs.
Player A looks at the prizes for two minutes.
Player A then gives the sheet of prizes to Player B.
Player A then has one minute to remember as many prizes as possible.
Player B ticks them off as Player A says them.
How many can you win?

LISTEN UP!

Prizes

Name:_____

Date:_____

Shopping list

I am planning my weekly shopping list.

Listen carefully to what I decide to buy.
Then tick off the items on the activity sheet.

1.   First I need some food for the children's tea.
      They could have fish fingers, with baked beans and oven chips.
      And for pudding I'll get them some yoghurts.

2.   Now, cleaning materials.
      We need some more washing-up liquid and a washing-up brush.
      We're also low on washing powder, so I'd better get some more.
      I think I'd better buy some more toilet cleaner too.

3.   I mustn't forget the pets.
      We need guinea pig food and some carrots.
      The cat needs some cat food.
      We've nearly run out of dog biscuits – I'll get some more.

4.   I think I'll make a cake this afternoon.
      I'd better buy some flour, eggs and sugar. I don't need margarine
      – we've already got plenty. I'll buy some cherries and make a
      cherry cake.

Extension

Work with a partner.

Look at the activity sheet and give your partner a list of six things you
need to buy.

Can your partner remember them all? Use the activity sheet as a
reminder.

LISTEN UP!

Shopping list

Name:_____ Date:_____

Dog biscuits ☐

Sugar ☐

Washing-up brush ☐

Lettuce ☐

Cherries ☐

Guinea pig food ☐

Bird seed ☐

Baked beans ☐

Floor cleaner ☐

Crisps ☐

Flour ☐

Washing powder ☐

Dog food ☐

Scouring pad ☐

Polish ☐

Carrots ☐

Sweets ☐

Pasta letters ☐

Margarine ☐

Fish fingers ☐

Toilet cleaner ☐

Cat food ☐

Raisins ☐

Sausages ☐

Chips ☐

Yoghurts ☐

Ice cream ☐

Washing-up liquid ☐

Butter ☐

Eggs ☐

LISTEN UP!

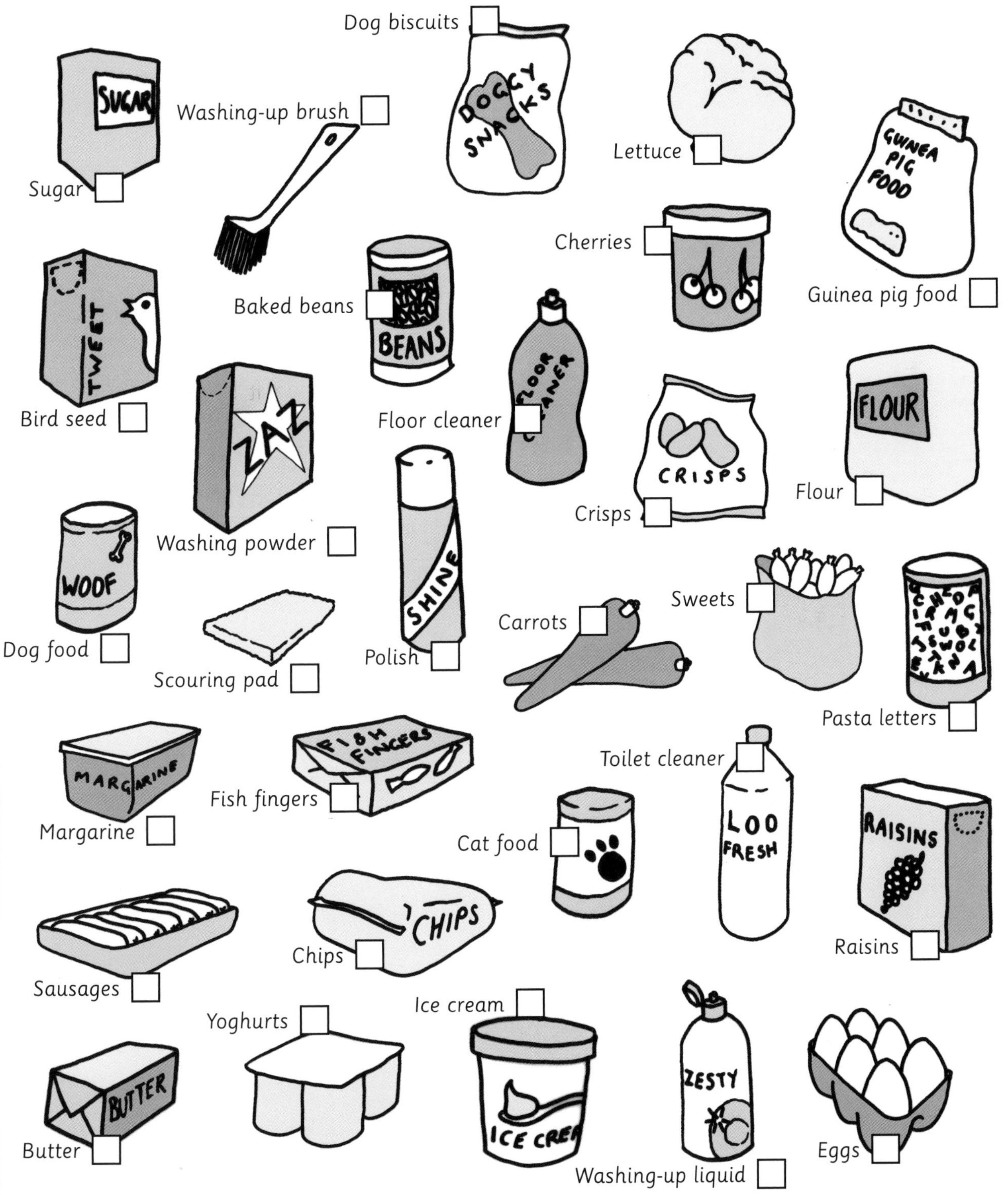

Making flapjacks

Listen to the description of making flapjacks.

Try to 'see' yourself collecting the items as they're mentioned.

This will help you to remember them and tick them off on the activity sheet.

Before I start I'll collect the utensils I'll need. First I'll need a large saucepan. Then I'll need a wooden spoon to mix the ingredients together. I'll need scales to weigh the ingredients, and a baking tray to cook the flapjacks on.

On the activity sheet, tick the items I need.

Now the ingredients. I'll get the margarine out of the fridge. I also need to get some brown sugar and some syrup. And I mustn't forget the porridge oats.

On the activity sheet, tick the ingredients I need.

Right, now I've got everything ready I can start.

First I need to melt the margarine in the saucepan.

Now that's melted I add the sugar and the syrup and stir it until the sugar dissolves.

Then I take the pan off the heat and pour in the porridge oats.

I mix it all together thoroughly.

Once it's all mixed I put the mixture on to the greased baking tray and flatten it down.

Now it's ready to go into the oven, for about 30 minutes.

Fill in the missing words on the activity sheet. Use some of the words from the box.

Extension

Make some flapjacks using your completed recipe.

LISTEN UP!

Making flapjacks

Name:_____   Date:_____

Utensils

☐   ☐   ☐   ☐   ☐   ☐

Ingredients

75g margarine   300g flour   1 tablespoon syrup   2 eggs   50g sugar   150g porridge oats

☐   ☐   ☐   ☐   ☐   ☐

Method

1. _____ the _____
   in the saucepan

2. Add the sugar and _____.
   Stir until the _____ dissolves.

3. Take the saucepan off
   the _____. Stir in the
   _____ _____.

4. Spread the mixture on the baking
   _____. Bake at gas mark 3
   (350°F/170°C) for ____ minutes.

| flour |
| 30 |
| melt |
| sugar |
| heat |
| syrup |
| table |
| porridge |
| rice |
| margarine |
| stir |
| oats |
| tray |

LISTEN UP!

Teacher's record sheet

Pupil name	Activities (tick when completed)																			
	1	2	3	4	5	6	7	8	9	10	11	12	13	14	15	16	17	18	19	20

LISTEN UP!

Pupil's record sheet

Name:_____   Date:_____

Activity	Date	How did I do?	How could I improve? (Choose 1–5 from the list below)
The monarchs' room			
The funfair			
Suspects			
The fall on Franwell Moor			
Shopping			
Class portraits			
Bags it's mine			
Caught speeding!			
Skateboard mix-up			
Flags			
Pizza party			
The race			
White elephant stall			
Nail art			
Chocolate box			
What am I?			
Join the dots			
Prizes			
Shopping list			
Making flapjacks			

1. Focus, concentrate and don't let myself be distracted.
2. Visualise – make a picture in my head, or 'take a photograph' of a scene.
3. Use association – link the items I need to remember.
4. Relax, but don't stop concentrating!
5. When I've forgotten something, let my mind wander around the things I remember, to see if it 'comes back' to me.

LISTEN UP!

LISTEN UP!

Awarded to

_____

for being a wonderful listener

Signed: _____

Date: _____

LISTEN UP!

Awarded to

_____

for being a wonderful listener

Signed: _____

Date: _____

Teacher's notes

LISTEN UP!

Teacher's notes

LISTEN UP!